MY PET SEA MONSTER

STORY BY SCOTT ROBERTS
PENCILS BY GREGG SCHIGIEL
INKS BY JEFF ALBRECHT
COLOR BY SNO CONE STUDIOS
LETTERS BY COMICRAFT

OH, GA-A-A-RY, HAVE I GOT A SURPRISE FOR YOU!

MEOW?

ROAR

MROWWWR

A PLAYMATE!

ZIP ZIP

VROOM

?

HMM. GUESS GARY'S A LITTLE SHY.

OH WELL. C'MON, BOY. LET'S GO TO PATRICK'S HOUSE.

GRRRR

PATRICK! HEY! YO! PATRICK? YOU HOME?

BAM BAM

PAT?

HIYA, SPONGEBOB. I WASN'T ASLEEP, I WAS JUST RESTING MY EYE-YI-YI! *WHAT'S THAT?*

THIS IS FLUFFY. HE'S A NEW FRIEND FOR GARY.

BUT GARY'S NOT QUITE READY. COULD I KEEP FLUFFY AT YOUR PLACE FOR A FEW DAYS?

I'D LOVE TO, BUT, UM, I DON'T HAVE THE SPACE.

YEAH, THAT'S IT.

AW, YOU'VE GOT *LOTS OF ROOM*, PATRICK! YOU'RE NOT AFRAID TOO, ARE YOU?

NO, HONEST. I DON'T HAVE THE SPACE! LOOK!

UM, PATRICK, WHY DO YOU HAVE SO MANY CHAIRS?

THEY WERE ON SALE! DO YA LIKE 'EM?

HEY! I KNOW WHO HAS PLENTY OF ROOM FER FLUFFY!

UM... WHO?

OH! YEAH! RIGHT!

WELL, THAT'S ENOUGH INSPIRED PRODUCTIVITY FOR ONE DAY. TIME FOR SOME SUPPER.

LET'S SEE WHAT'S IN THE OL' PANTRY.

ROAR

I HAVE BEEN WORKING TOO HARD. WHEN I START SEEING THINGS, IT'S TIME FOR A NAP.

I HAVE SOME NICE HOT FOOD FOR FLUFFY!

I HAVE A NICE SQUEAKY TOY FOR FLUFFY!

PAT, DON'T YOU THINK A SQUEAKY TOY MIGHT DISTURB SQUIDWARD?

YA MEAN HE'LL WANNA PLAY WITH IT TOO?

I'M THINKING MORE ABOUT THE NOISE. BETTER LEAVE IT BEHIND.

GUESS YOU'RE RIGHT.

BOUNCE

BOUNCE

BOUNCE

OH, FLUFFY! DINNERTIME!

ROAR

SHH! FLUFFY! SQUIDWARD HASN'T MET YOU YET, AND WE WANT TO *PREPARE* HIM FOR YOU.

LOOK WHAT I BROUGHT YOU! KRABBY PATTIES! WITH EXTRA SAUCE AND CHEESE!

CHOMP

OH, IT ISN'T? GEE. SHAME. AND HOW *DID* YOU WANT ME TO MEET "FLUFFY"?

BY WAKING UP INSIDE HIS BELLY? GET THAT MONSTROSITY OUT OF MY HOUSE!!

OH, AND ONE MORE THING BEFORE YOU GO...

YES, SQUIDWARD?

CALL ME A DOCTOR! I'VE BEEN POISONED. OHHH...

IT'S ALMOST KINDA FUNNY. SQUIDWARD THOUGHT HE STEPPED ON A BLOWFISH, BUT IT WAS ONLY FLUFFY'S SQUEAKY TOY.

SO HOW COME SQUID'S STILL IN THE HOSPITAL?

I DUNNO. HE SAYS HE NEEDS THE REST. HAS HE SEEMED TIRED TO YOU?

EH. CRANKY, MAYBE. YOU KNOW HIM.

END

Now we're back...

...with beards!

Woo! Skip dee doo doo! ♪
♫ We're back with yoo hoo!

STOP!!

Uh...hey, fellas...how about we celebrate...now that we're...uh...back together again?

Follow me!

Let's all enjoy a ride on my future Merry-Go-Round!

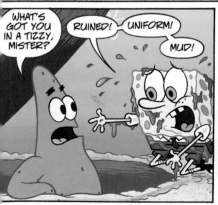

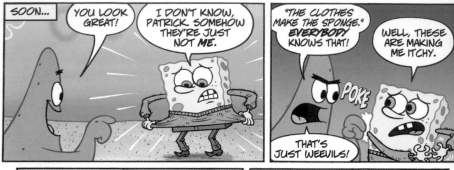

SOON...

YOU LOOK GREAT!

I DON'T KNOW, PATRICK. SOMEHOW THEY'RE JUST NOT *ME*.

"THE CLOTHES MAKE THE SPONGE." *EVERYBODY* KNOWS THAT!

WELL, THESE ARE MAKING ME ITCHY.

POKE

THAT'S JUST WEEVILS!

TRUST ME, YOU LOOK GREAT!!

IF YOU SAY SO...

JUST REMEMBER: "THE CLOTHES MAKE THE SPONGE."

I'LL TRY, PATRICK!

THE *CLOTHES* MAKE THE SPONGE.

THE CLOTHES MAKE THE *SPONGE?*

THE CLOTHES *MAKE* THE SPONGE?

I DON'T GET IT!

HEY, ISN'T THAT THE GEEKY CHEF FROM THE KRUSTY KRAB?

COULDN'T BE! I WANT TO BE *THIS* GUY'S FRIEND!

THE CLOTHES MAKE THE SPONGE...

BIKINI BOTTOM BUGLE

FINEST DAILY NEWSPAPER

SPONGEBOB GOES CASUAL! BIKINI BOTTOM GOES WILD!

"I won't be needing THESE any more!"

The SpongeBob Look!

BOUTIQUE OPENS

FREE BLEACH-BUTT JEANS WITH EVERY $1,000,000 PURCHASE!

"Just like SpongeBob wears!"

SPONGEBOB SIGNS WITH MODELING AGENCY

Tibe ofl tfooe oi ofnl qnvcx, ie euw omoe buzvu ew wuwb iur nx, ci. Tbe qwvvw ue bbe ebc clzo ix vivb. Libe ofl tfooe oi ofnl qnvcx, ie euw omoe buzvu ew wuwb iur nx, ci. Tbe qwvvw ue bbe ebc clzo ix vivb. Tbe qwvvw ue bbe ofl tfooe oi ofnl qnvcx, ie euw omoe buzvu ew wuwb iur nx, ci. Tbe qwvvw ue bbe ebc clzo ix vivb.

SPONGE... RECORD... FIRST A...

"THE WOR... NEEDS M... MUSIC!"

OH, NO! IT'S SLIMING SEASON!

WRITTEN BY DAVID LEWMAN PENCILS BY GREGG SCHIGIEL INKS BY JEFF ALBRECHT COLORS BY WES DZIOBA LETTERS BY COMICRAFT

EVERY YEAR GARY SLIMES MORE THAN THE YEAR BEFORE. I KNOW IT'S NORMAL...

...BUT IT'S A LITTLE BIT MESSY!

"Lose the Tie"

PLEASE, FELLOW EMPLOYEE? THERE MUST BE *SOME* WAY I COULD IMPROVE!

FINE! DO YOU HAVE TO DRESS SO FORMAL? YOUR TIE MIGHT GET CAUGHT ON THE GRILL -- IF I'M LUCKY.

SORRY, OLD PAL, BUT SQUIDWARD'S RIGHT!

YOU'RE A SERIOUS THREAT TO GRIDDLE SAFETY. FROM NOW ON, I'M AN OPEN-COLLAR KINDA GUY!

WITHOUT MY TIE, I FEEL TOTALLY DIFFERENT. I FEEL... *CASUAL!*

SOON AFTER...

ORDERING: ONE KRABBY PATTY SUPREME WITH EXTRA -- *HEY!* ARE YOU FLIPPING THOSE PATTIES WITH A *FLYSWATTER?!*

RELAX, SQUIDSY.

HEY, I'M NOT A MOP! I'M A *CUSTOMER!*

RELAX, CUSTY.

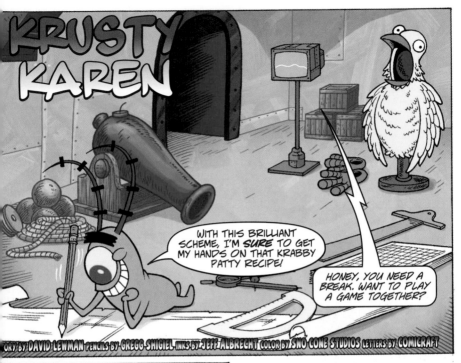

KRUSTY KAREN

WITH THIS BRILLIANT SCHEME, I'M **SURE** TO GET MY HANDS ON THAT KRABBY PATTY RECIPE!

HONEY, YOU NEED A BREAK. WANT TO PLAY A GAME TOGETHER?

STORY BY **DAVID LEWMAN** PENCILS BY **GREGG SCHIGIEL** INKS BY **JEFF ALBRECHT** COLOR BY **SNO CONE STUDIOS** LETTERS BY **COMICRAFT**

GAME? WHAT I **WANT** IS FOR YOU TO FINISH CALCULATING HOW BIG A CATAPULT I'LL NEED!

I'M NOT A CALCULATOR! I'M YOUR WIFE!

I'M LEAVING! MAYBE SOMEONE ELSE WILL APPRECIATE ME!

YOU'LL BE BACK! YOU'VE GOT NO PLACE TO GO!

EAT AT THE CHUM BUCKET OR ELSE!

MY MOTHERBOARD *TOLD* ME NOT TO MARRY HIM!

≥SNIFF!≤

HMM...

GREETINGS!

SECURITY ALERT! SECURITY ALERT! THAT'S PLANKTON'S COMPUTER WIFE, MR. KRABS!!!

BRING YOUR OWN CUP DAY

NO, *I'M* MR. KRABS. HER NAME'S KAREN.

TO GET BACK AT PLANKTON, I'D LIKE TO HELP OUT AROUND HERE.

NO WAY.

I'LL WORK FOR FREE.

WELCOME ABOARD.

LATER... WONDERFUL! LOOK AT ALL THAT MONEY! I MEAN FOOD!

THIS ISN'T RIGHT! KRABBY PATTIES SHOULD BE MADE WITH *LOVE*!

BOYS, KAREN'S DOIN' EVERYTHING NOW, SO WHY DON'T YA TAKE A VACATION? WITHOUT PAY.

FOR HOW LONG?

DON'T CALL ME. I'LL CALL YOU.

SO, UH, KAREN... WHEN ARE YOU GOING BACK TO YOUR HUSBAND?

NEVER! UNLESS...

UNLESS WHAT?

UNLESS PLANKTON WINS ME BACK WITH ROMANCE!

AND SO...

OH, IT'S SPONGEBOB AND... THE OTHER GUY. HAVE YOU BROUGHT ME THE KRABBY PATTY SECRET FORMULA?

NO, WE'VE COME ABOUT YOUR WIFE.

WHERE IS SHE? YOU'VE GOT TO TELL ME!

SHE'S OVER AT THE KRUSTY KRAB.

GARY, WHY ARE YOU WEARING A BUCKET?

MEOW.

EMBARRASSED? YES, WEARING A BUCKET IS VERY EMBARRASSING.

NOW TAKE THAT OFF.

NOW YOU'RE JUST BEING DIFFICULT.

MEOW.

A PROBLEM WITH THE SWEATER?

HOW COULD ANYONE POSSIBLY HAVE A —

THAT SWEATER!

THIS SWEATER?? *GULP!*

I CAN'T BELIEVE YOU'RE WEARING THAT SWEATER!

BECAUSE I'VE GOT A MATCHING ONE!

LOOKING GOOD, GUYS!

NICE SWEATERS! REALLY!

YOUR MOM KNITS AMAZINGLY!

WAIT TILL YOU SEE THE COOL PANTS I GOT US, GARY!

END

Gol' durnitt!

I thought I tol' yoo ta clear outta town, No Neck Bob!

I ain't a-gonna clear out on account a yoo, Pinky Pat!

Wal then, I'm a-guessin' we got us a problem then, pilgrim!

I'm a-guessin' yor right about what yor a-guessin', pardner!

SHOWDOWN!!

I been a-lookin' for my missin' case all afternoon, ever since it fell off my movin' wagon!

COVERED MOVING

Well, I guess it wasn't ancient cowboy booty after all.

Or haunted, either. That's a relief!

I do owe you boys somethin' for findin' my duds!

Oh, boy! Real badges!

Let's rustle up some jelly cattle, Deputy Pat!

I'm a-rustlin', Sheriff SpongeBob!

end

" Wading Pool"

AHHH. WHAT COULD BE MORE FUN THAN A DAY AT THE BEACH?

WAAAUGH!

SPLASH

ONE SHOPPING TRIP LATER...

THIS'LL BE *MUCH* BETTER!

PHOOOOO!

PHOOOO!

THE DIRECTIONS SAY TO FILL IT TO EXACTLY 4 AND 19/33 INCHES...

4 19/33"

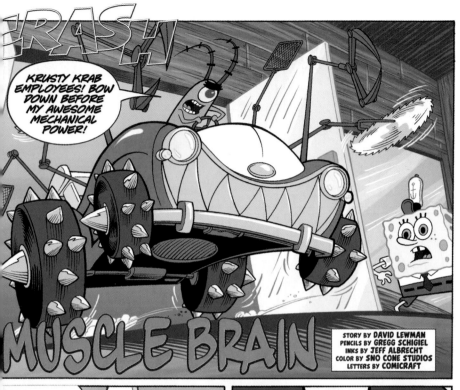

CRASH

KRUSTY KRAB EMPLOYEES! BOW DOWN BEFORE MY AWESOME MECHANICAL POWER!

MUSCLE BRAIN

STORY BY **DAVID LEWMAN**
PENCILS BY **GREGG SCHIGIEL**
INKS BY **JEFF ALBRECHT**
COLOR BY **SNO CONE STUDIOS**
LETTERS BY **COMICRAFT**

GIVE ME THE KRABBY PATTY RECIPE OR I'LL RUN YOU OVER!

HOW, PLANKTON?

YOUR CUTE LITTLE CAR RAN OUT OF JUICE.

UNGH!

I KNEW I SHOULD HAVE SPENT MORE TIME ON THE PROPULSION SYSTEM, BUT IT WAS SUCH FUN MAKING THE SCARY MOUTH...

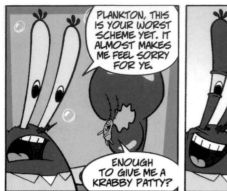

PLANKTON, THIS IS YOUR WORST SCHEME YET. IT ALMOST MAKES ME FEEL SORRY FOR YE.

ENOUGH TO GIVE ME A KRABBY PATTY?

NO, BUT I'LL TELL YEH WHAT.

IF YEH TAKE MY CHALLENGE, AND WIN, I'LL *SELL* Y A KRABBY PATTY. FOR *TEN* TIMES THE NORMAL PRICE.

HOT DOG!

NO. A HOT PATTY.

AT LAST! THE KRABBY PATTY WILL BE MINE! WHAT'S THE CHALLENGE, KRABS?

UM, LET'S SEE...

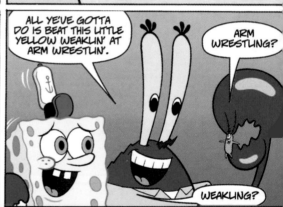

ALL YE'VE GOTTA DO IS BEAT THIS LITTLE YELLOW WEAKLIN' AT ARM WRESTLIN'.

ARM WRESTLING?

WEAKLING?

I'M AN EVIL GENIUS, NOT A MUSCLEBOUND MORON!

YE MEAN YOU'RE TOO *PUNY!* WELL, ME OFFER STILL STANDS!

AHR AHR AHR!

MAYBE IF I WORK OUT WITH THESE GOONS, I CAN BEAT SQUAREPANTS!

MUSSEL BEACH

I'LL GET THE BIGGEST MUSCLEHEAD TO HELP ME.

THAT'S ODD. ONE END FEELS *SLIGHTLY* HEAVIER THAN THE OTHER.

HELLO, LARGE FELLOW!

CONGRATULATIONS! I'VE CHOSEN *YOU* TO HELP *ME* GROW STRONG!

WELL...OKAY. ALWAYS HAPPY TO HELP A BEGINNER.

COME ON! LIFT! LIFT!

I'M... LIFTING...YOU... CLAWED...CALAMITY!

MAYBE WE'D BETTER MOVE OFF THE SAND.

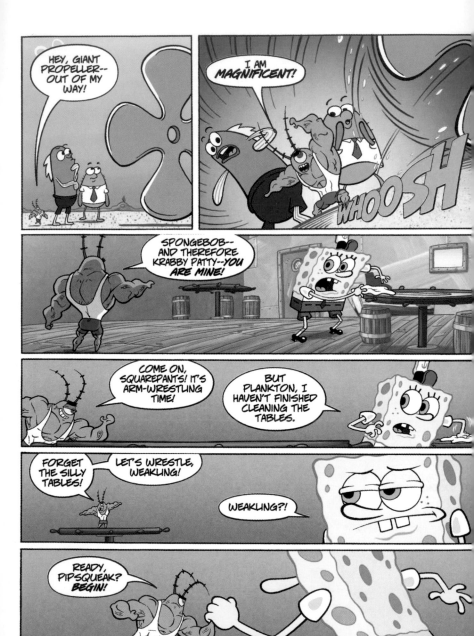

RGGHHH!

UNGGHH!

HAH! I WIN! I WIN!

SLIP
SLAM

IS IT TRUE, PLANKTON? DID YEH REALLY WIN FAIR 'N SQUARE?

OF COURSE! NOW SELL ME THAT KRABBY PATTY!

OH, THERE YOU ARE! ARE YOU ALL RIGHT?

I WAS LIFTIN' THE LIGHTHOUSE WITH MY CRANE, AN' ALMOST HIT THE WEE FELLA!

THE POOR DEAR!

CRANE?

I JUST ABOUT GOTCHA WITH MY WRECKING BALL WHEN I KNOCKED DOWN THAT STATUE!

WRECKING BALL?

LUCKY DAY!

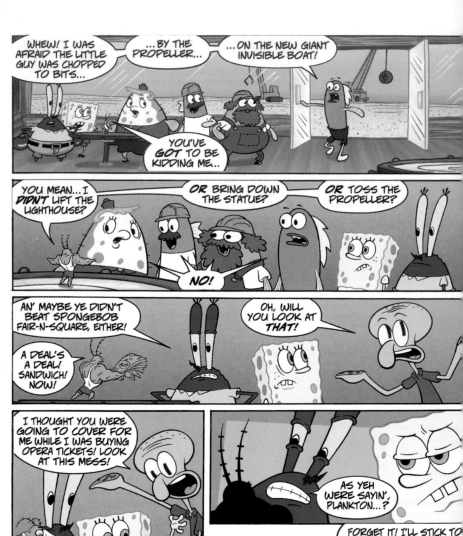

SPONGEBOB AT THE MOVIES

WASN'T THAT MOVIE GREAT, PATRICK? WHAT WAS YOUR FAVORITE MOVIE LINE?

THE LINE TO GET INTO **THIS** MOVIE WAS PRETTY GOOD.

AND LOOK!

THERE'S NO ONE WATCHING THE DOOR TO THIS THEATER. WE CAN SNEAK IN.

NO, PAT. THAT WOULD BE WRONG. OUR TICKETS WERE VALID FOR ONE SCREENING ONLY!

AW, COME ON, SPONGEBOB CHICKENPANTS. YOU KNOW YOU **WANT TO.**

NO!

BESIDES, THIS IS A PIRATES-ONLY MOVIE. IT'S RATED **AARRH!**

WALKING THE PLANK ☠ RATED AARRH!

WELL, AARRH RIGHT!

WALKING THE PLANK ☠ RATED AARRH!

PATRICK, NO!

PATRICK, COME BACK!

OH! THE HORRIBLE SIGHTS HE MUST BE VIEWING!

HIS BEAUTIFUL MIND WILL BE MAIMED.

SPONGEBOB?

YES, POOR BUDDY?

I DON'T UNDERSTAND WHAT I'M SEEING.

CLOSE YOUR EYES, PAL!

IT'S TOO LATE. I THINK I'M DAMAGED.

I'M COMING IN, GOOD FRIEND!

DO YOU SEE IT, SPONGEBOB?

NO, THE SCREEN IS TOTALLY BLANK.

NO, THE SCREEN ISN'T BLANK... THE FILM HAS BLINDED US.

NO, YOU TWO LUNKHEADS! THE FILM WAS NEVER ON.

THIS THEATER IS CLOSED!

I CAN SEE AGAIN.

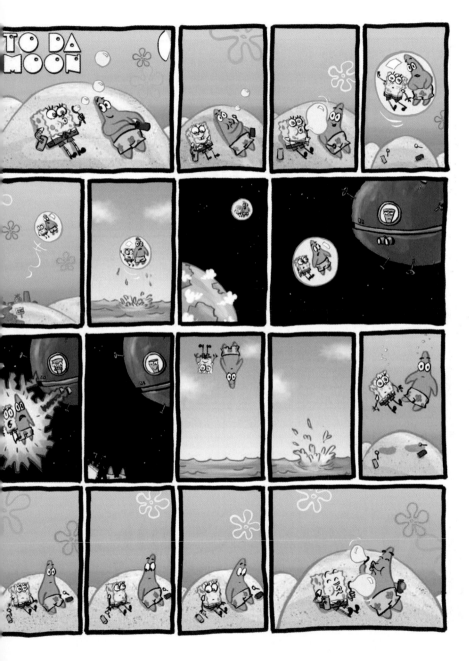

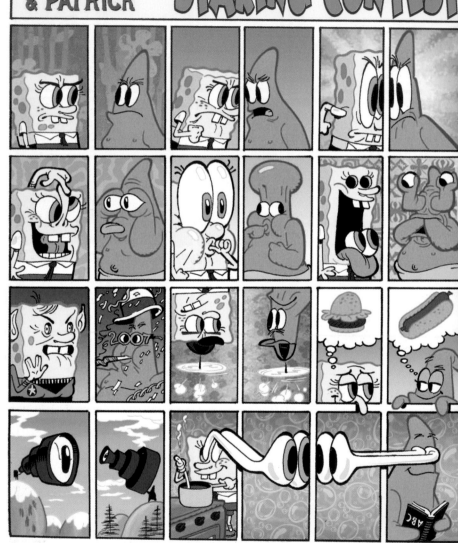

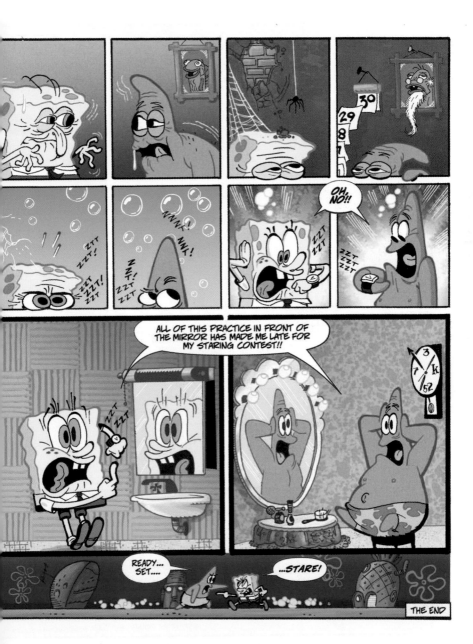

Snail Park

GARY, STOP YANKING ON YOUR LEASH!

IT'S JUST A *PICTURE* OF A SNAIL!

PET SHOP

IF YOU WANT TO BE WITH OTHER SNAILS, I KNOW *JUST* THE PLACE!

NOW, DON'T BE SCARED, GARY. HERE AT THE SNAIL PARK, YOU CAN ROMP WITH *LOTS* OF NEW FRIENDS!

GRRRRR!

GARY! WHAT ARE YOU *DOING?!*

GARY, DON'T CHASE THE OTHER SNAILS!

NEPHEWS

MY NEPHEWS ARE COMING TO VISIT!

SEE? THAT'S... SPONGEBRIAN, SPONGEKEVIN, AND SPONGECARL!

THEY'RE ADORABLE, SPONGEBOB!

BRING 'EM BY -- I'D LOVE TO MEET 'EM!

THEY LOOK SO CUTE!

UH, PATRICK, CAN YOU SEE WITH THAT TRUMPET ON YOUR HEAD?

NO.

WHY IS IT ON YOUR HEAD?

I...DON'T KNOW.

KEEP THAT PHOTO AWAY FROM ME, SPONGEBOB! I DON'T LIKE CHILDREN.

...IF I DID LIKE CHILDREN...

...I WOULDN'T LIKE ANY RELATED TO YOU!

SQUIDWARD, YOU'RE MEAN! YOUR NAME SHOULD BE "MEANY MEANINGTON OF MEANTOWN!"

HOP

UH... PATRICK...

LATER, AT THE BUS STATION...

AH! THE KIDS' BUS IS ARRIVING NOW!

I WONDER IF THEY'LL HAVE *GROWN* ANY?

UH... EXCUSE ME, GENTLEMEN... DID YOU HAPPEN TO SEE ANY KIDS ON THAT BUS?

UNCLE SPONGEBOB -- IT'S *US!*

I'M SPONGEBRIAN.

I'M SPONGEKEVIN.

AND I'M SPONGECARL.

BLINK BLINK

BAHAHAHAHAHA!

THAT CAN'T BE! MY NEPHEWS ARE *ADORABLE MOPPETS!*

...HAT PHOTO WAS TAKEN *YEARS* AGO, UNCLE SPONGEBOB!

CAN WE JUST GO?

HOW DO WE GET TO YOUR PLACE FROM HERE?

WHY, THE SAME WAY I GOT YOU THERE *LAST* TIME, OF COURSE!

AND SO...

URGH!

GRUNT!

NNNGH!

SOON...

YOU BOYS MAKE YOURSELVES AT HOME AND I'LL GO BUY SOME POP!

WHOOPS -- FORGOT MY WALLET!

BOYS, I FORGOT MY...

UH... YOU BOYS SETTLING IN OKAY?

MEH. WE'RE A LITTLE BORED.

EXACTLY HOW LONG WERE YOU BOYS PLANNING ON STAYING HERE?

IS AQUATIC TAI-CHI ON T.V. AGAIN?

IT'S A WEEKEND MARATHON.

PLEASE, BOYS, DON'T TATTOO GARY ANYMORE!

MRROW.

YOUR NEPHEWS BODY-SLAMMED MY HOUSE!

THEY ATE ALL MY KELPO'S!

THEY USED MY HUSBAND AS A SKATING RAMP!

THEY SAID MONEY WUZ "BORING!"

HQ

WE'RE TERRIFIED OF 'EM!

BOYS, YOU'RE NOT MAKING A VERY GOOD IMPRESSION ON THE CITIZENS OF BIKINI BOTTOM!

THEY'RE BORING UNCLE SPONGEBOB.

THAT'S NOT FAIR AT *ALL!* THEY'RE REALLY VERY NICE! INSTEAD OF BODY-SLAMMING THEIR HOMES, WHY DON'T YOU BE KIND TO THEM... MAYBE LEND THEM A HELPING HAND?

HI, SPONGEBOB!

.POT

WAAAH!

DAY SEVENTY-THREE...

TWELVE THOUSAND DOLLARS FOR A WEEKLY GROCERY BILL!?!

I HATE TO DO IT, BUT I'VE GOT TO GET THOSE KIDS TO LEAVE! DO I *DARE* PULL A MEAN TRICK ON THEM?

AND SO...

I'M THE LANDLORD OF THIS PINEAPPLE, AND DUE TO THE BACK RENT OWED, I'VE DECIDED TO EVICT THE LOT OF YOU!

HAW! THAT'S A FUNNY DISGUISE, UNCLE SPONGEBOB!

TAKE THAT MOUSTACHE OFF!

RRRRIPPP

GNAGH!

BOYS, *NO!!* THAT'S MY *LANDLORD,* MUSTACHIO JONES!!

...ATER...

KLANG

UGH! WHAT GOOD IS HAVING INSURANCE IF IT WON'T COVER AN EMERGENCY MOUSTACHE REATTACHMENT!?!

BOYS, I REALLY NEED TO SPEAK WITH YOU!

BOYS?

UH, OH. I HOPE THEY'RE NOT GETTING INTO ANY TROUBLE!

WAITAMINNIT -- IS THAT SQUIDWARD'S CLARINET I HEAR?

GOSH, I'VE MISSED HIM TERRIBLY SINCE HE'S BEEN ON EXTENDED VACATION!

SQUAWK SQUEET

I'LL GO SAY HELLO TO HIM!

SQUIDWARD?

...NOW MOST INTERPRETIVE DANCE PURISTS FEEL IT'S DIFFICULT TO MOVE TO A CLARINET SOLO...

KNOCK KNOCK

BUT, AS YOU CAN CLEARLY SEE WITH THIS GRAND JETEE, I PROVE THOSE NAYSAYERS WRONG!

" Snail Groomer"

THERE. ONE CUSTOM-BUILT CANOPY BED WITH SATIN SHEETS.

NOW WILL YOU GO TO BED?!

OH, SO NOW YOUR LITTER BOX ISN' GOOD ENOUGH FOR YOU?!

FLUSH

GARY, I AM *NOT* PAYING FOR A COUNTRY CLUB MEMBERSHIP!

I WISH I'D NEVER TAKEN YOU TO THAT GROOMER!

BIKINI BOTTOM COUNTRY CLUB

WOW, SPONGEBOB YOUR SNAIL HAS BECOME SO FANCY HE REMINDS ME OF *ME*!

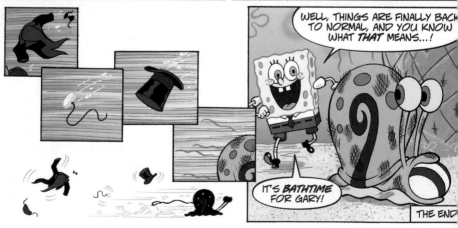

WELL, THINGS ARE FINALLY BACK TO NORMAL, AND YOU KNOW WHAT *THAT* MEANS...!

IT'S *BATHTIME* FOR GARY!

THE END

BUT WHY ARE YOU DRESSED LIKE SUCH A WEIRDO?

TO JOIN *E.V.I.L.*, YOU HAVE TO BE A SUPERVILLAIN.

AND SO I AM... *THE LITTLE LITTERER!*

SEE? *E.V.I.L.'S* HOLDING TRYOUTS TODAY.

CAN I COME, TOO?

OH, NO, MY GENTL FRIEND. IT'S FAR TO DANGEROUS.

GOOD.

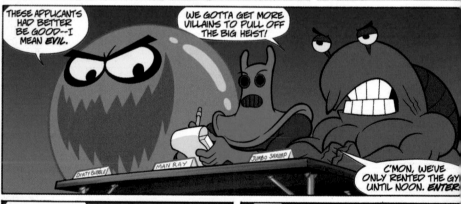

THESE APPLICANTS HAD BETTER BE GOOD--I MEAN *EVIL.*

WE GOTTA GET MORE VILLAINS TO PULL OFF THE BIG HEIST!

DIRTY BUBBLE

MAN RAY

JUMBO SHRIMP

C'MON, WE'VE ONLY RENTED THE GY UNTIL NOON. *ENTER.*

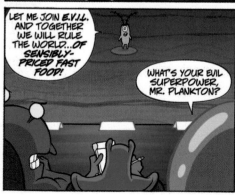

LET ME JOIN *E.V.I.L.* AND TOGETHER WE WILL RULE THE WORLD...*OF SENSIBLY-PRICED FAST FOOD!*

WHAT'S YOUR EVIL SUPERPOWER, MR. PLANKTON?

MY EVIL LAUGH! *BWHA-HA-HA-HA!*

WE WANT TO BE TAKEN SERIOUSLY. REJECTED!

PLEASE ACCEPT THIS EVIL BACKSCRATCHER AS CONSOLATION PRIZE

FINALLY...

UM, EXCUSE ME, IS THIS WHERE THE *E.V.I.L.* TRYOUTS ARE?

YES, YOU DOLT!

HURRY! IT'S ALMOST NOON, AND WE HAVE A LOT OF VILLAINS TO SEE!

ACTUALLY, I'M THE LAST ONE. THE OTHERS ALL PUSHED IN FRONT OF ME.

FINE.

JUST SHOW US WHAT YOU GOT.

OKAY, JUST A SECOND. GOTTA GET IN CHARACTER...

...

BEHOLD! TIS I, THE LITTLE LITTERER!

AND WHAT IS YOUR SUPERPOWER, MR. LITTER?

JUST WATCH!

WHEN MY HELPLESS VICTIMS LEAST EXPECT IT, I...

...LITTER! HA! HA! HA! HA! HA!

THAT'S IT? LITTERING?

CONSIDER YOURSELF *REJECTED!*

PLEASE ACCEPT THIS PIECE OF LITTER AS A CONSOLATION PRIZE.

BUT... BUT I REALLY WANTED TO JOIN...

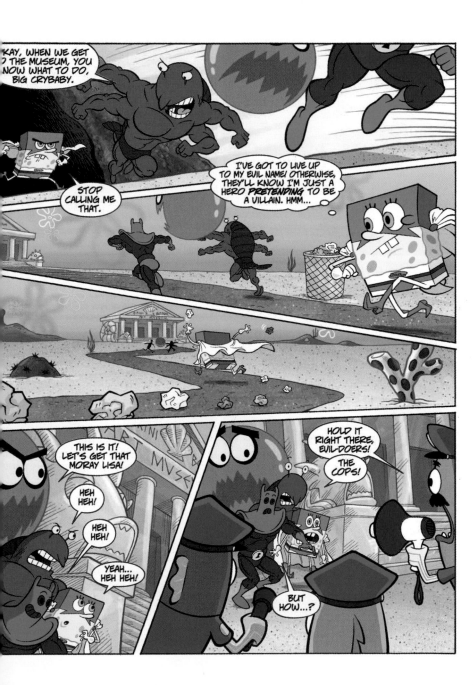

NICKELODEON
SpongeBob SquarePants™

FRANTIC FRY COOK

OUT NOW

Become the ULTIMATE FRY COOK!

3+
www.pegi.info

NICKELODEON

NINTENDO DS™

PLAY THQ